KU-101-851

Maev 'n' Rick

700039649532

'Dogs of Rock' are original characters
from 'Make over Mutts 2008 Calendar
© Icarus Arts Publishing Ltd
'Make over Mechanics 2010 Calendar
© Maverick Arts Publishing Ltd

Post production - Paul Cocken,
Authors - Paul Messis, Steve Bicknell

Graphic Concepts - Frankie Nally

Design - Ed Gover

Additional Photo Credits
Battle of the Bands Girl Singer,
Licenced by 'I Love Images'

Fan Club Page-Crowd Photo
by John Linton/Rex Features
Crowd by Naki /PMYCA/Rex Features

**PUBLISHED BY MAVERICK ARTS
PUBLISHING LTD**

Studio 4,
Hardham Mill Park,
Pulborough,
RH20 1LA
+44(0) 1798 875980

©Maverick Arts Publishing Limited (2010)

ISBN 978-1-84886-041-4

Maverick
arts publishing

www.maverickartsclub.com

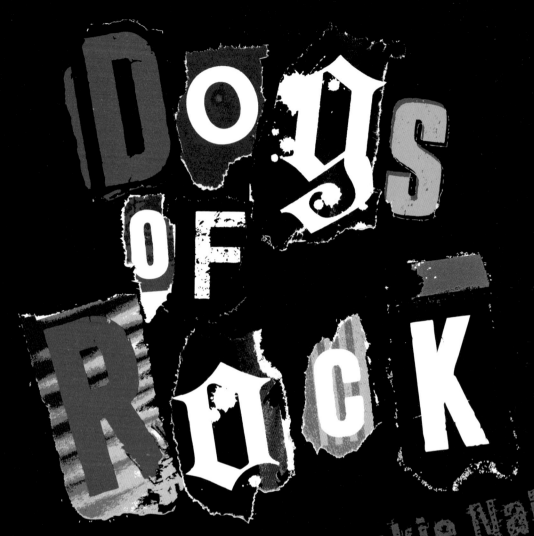

Dogs of Rock

Paul Cocken – Frankie Nally
Steve Bicknell – Paul Messis

Our Story

We met at Uni way back in the eighties, hanging out with a bunch of Dudes, well into the sounds..

Lost touch... bummed around the world.. met up years later in OZ. One night, very late after a heavy session Jamming together.. sounded good.... felt good.. ....the Dogs of Rock were BORN.. ....the rest is History

Rick

Our First Gig

A village hall in the middle of nowhere....Great venue for a christening.... Rubbish for our first gig...

....nobody came!

DOGS OF ROCK

Crank it up Marv...

MOVIN ON UP...

It got much BETTER. In the Final of Battle of the Bands, Rick rustled up his mates and quite a few birds to vote for us.

We're in the FINALS

LET'S BLOW THE HOUSE DOWN...

BATTLE OF THE BANDS
GRAND PRIZE
A CHANCE TO
JANUARY 24th
Wailing high school
7pm till 9pm
EMAIL
shopwithmarvandrick.com

Who is this **pretender?**
She stands no chance against us...
"Come on Love ... Move over ....
....Let the **big boys in"**

Once we'd been **noticed** everything moved so fast. Winning the Battle of the Bands got us loads of gigs.

WE went wild every night... Even splashed out for new gear.

Now we have been signed......it's ....crazy man.

We've been signed

Dogs of Rock

- ## HOME
- ## GIG LIST
- ## TICKETS
- ## FAN CLUB

- CONTESTS
- LINKS
- CLIPS
- GIFTS
- STORE

WELCOME Follow the news and views of Rick & Marv

NEW TOUR DATES ADDED

OFFICIAL TEE SHIRTS

Available in three sizes. 100% cotton.

White only.

CLICK HERE TO ORDER

Join the Fan Club

News of the Band, video clips
tickets, gifts, signed books
from the Marv & Rick....

JOIN NOW....
www.dogsofrockfanclub.org

We're The Dogs

Intro C | G | A | A   x 4

Verse 1

C   G   A   A
We're walkin' down the street

"   "   "   "
And we haven't got a leash

"   "   "   "
We're the coolest dogs in town

F   G   E
And we're gonna turn your world upside down

Chorus

C   G   A   A
We're the Dogs (Dogs of Rock) ← *Backing vocals*
We're The Dogs (Dog's of Rock)
We're The Dogs (Dogs of Rock)

F   G   E
And we're gonna turn your world upside down.

Verse 2

C   G   A   A
Well we've seen this little toy dog

"   "   "   "
She's the prettiest poodle in the whole scene

"   "   "   "
We're the coolest dogs in town

F   G   E
But she still treats us mean

D   A
We're the Dogs (Dogs of Rock)
We're The Dogs (Dog's of Rock)
We're The Dogs (Dogs of Rock)

CHORUS

F   G   E
And we're gonna turn your world upside down.

GUITAR SOLO – over   C | G | A | A   × 8

C   G   A   A
We're gonna leave the kennel
So we can play all around

VERSE 3

F   G   E
We're the coolest dogs in town
And we're gonna play real loud

D   C   A
We're the Dogs (Dogs of Rock)
We're The Dogs (Dog's of Rock)
We're The Dogs (Dogs of Rock)

Chorus

F   G   E
And we're gonna turn your world upside down.

end

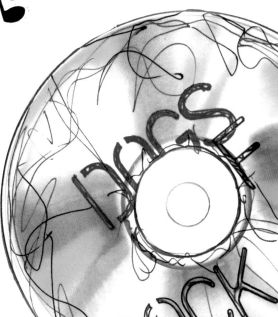

MUSIC BY RICK
LYRICS BY MARV

OUR FIRST TOUR

The lights.. **the screams** ...the heat ...the sweat
we **played** all night...

Best **Buzz** we have ever had...

TOUR DATES

CabaretVizsla, Edinburgh
Wetnose, Gateshead
The Dogpit, Leeds
TheDogHouse, Manchester
The Rocking Dog Derby
The Barkmender, Northampton
Hail and Wail, Cambridge
Norwich Bonemasters
Dogie Hogie, Brighton
Wailing Joe's, Guildford
Footpads, Portsmouth
Club Ifor Bark, Cardiff
The Hounds, Birmingham
Marrow Bones
High Wycombe 100 Tails
London
Barking Academy

gig after gig...
town after town...
sleep all day...
crazy all night...

Dogs of Rock...
keep doing it...
all night long...

DOGS OF ROCK

Feeling like Rock Stars!
Flying High!

DOGS OF ROCK

Hey RICK – "who would have thought your old dribble would now be worth proper dosh..."

Live at the **BARKING ACADEMY**

Battle of
the bands
WINNERS...

**DOGS
OF
ROCK**

doors open 9pm

Tickets £10.00 avilable from venue
hotline: 084500 76003 9800
address bone road, dog bedford. DO15 G22
A Big Noise Production presented by Growlinghound
book on-line www.ticketbuyer.co.uk

Friday

26th November

THEY
LOVED
US!

best set...
sounds...
...gig...crew...
crowd... on Tour

Well it's the end of our first tour.
Time to get down to some serious partying...
Thanks for coming along...
sees yer next time.

MARV & RICK